RELAXING
DOT-TO-DOT
UNDER THE SEA

SEVENOAKS

Introduction

Welcome to a new challenge, *Relaxing Dot-to-Dot: Under the Sea*! Here is a collection of what can be found deep in the oceans or in the shallows near the coast. You'll learn about the largest animal that has ever existed and about the small creatures that make the beautiful shells we collect on the beach. To reveal each creature, you'll have to join together at least 1,001 numbered dots. That's certain to take time, and you will need to concentrate. Think of this as your opportunity to shut down the laptop, and make sure you turn off the television. You don't want any distractions—the point of these puzzles is to help you relax.

Life underwater is diverse and extraordinary. Today's seas contain creatures that were found in seas before dinosaurs walked the earth. Some creatures that were assumed to be extinct have been rediscovered. Other creatures have been discovered only in the past couple of years.

Revealing the images on some pages will be difficult. Sometimes the dots are massed together. Where they are, we've used darker colors for numbers to guide you. And if you do get stuck, all the solutions are printed at the back of the book. As you reveal each picture, you'll learn about creatures without a brain, and creatures that can hold their breath for hours. You'll learn about creatures that can grow back a limb they've lost, and how creatures can see in the dark. And you'll learn exactly what makes a fish a fish—and why some "fish" aren't.

Completing all the images in the book will mean joining together more than 40,000 dots. However, don't be daunted. Think of this as more than 40,000 ways to relax. So sharpen your pencils, and get ready to explore the world waiting for you *Under the Sea*.

1. Jellyfish

Found today in every ocean, jellyfish are at least 500 million years old. In the center of their umbrella-shape, smooth body lies their mouth, by which they feed and also expel their waste. They capture their prey in their tentacles. They have no brain, heart, bones, or eyes. Some species have ocelli, "eyes" that do not see but that can detect light and sometimes color.

2. Sea Horse

Let's get this straight: Sea horses are fish, being that they breathe through their gills and have a swim bladder. However, they are poor swimmers. The dwarf sea horse has a top speed of 5 feet (1.5 meters) per hour. Sea horses propel themselves through the water by using their dorsal fin, which beats up to 70 times per second, while their pectoral fins help them steer.

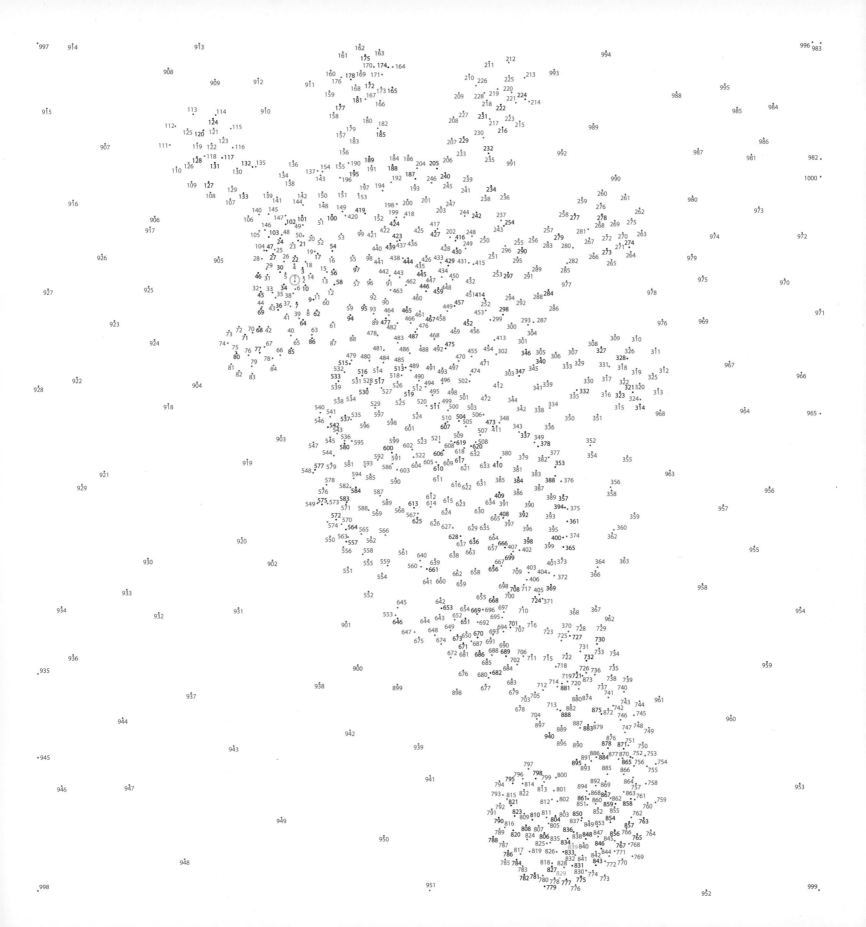

3. Blue Whale

The blue whale is the largest animal ever to have existed. When newly born, it is more than 26 feet (8 meters) long and weighs up to 5,950 pounds (2,700 kilograms). For comparison, a large truck weighs about 500 pounds (225 kilograms) less. When fully grown, the whale is about 100 feet (30 meters) long and weighs up to 210 tons (190 metric tons). It's difficult to provide comparison. The African elephant is the largest mammal on land and weighs less than 7 tons (6.25 metric tons).

4. Torpedo Ray

The torpedo ray can emit electricity for defense or attack. It stores its electricity in its tissues, much as a battery does, and calculates how much energy it needs to release to capture its prey. The shock can be enough to leave an adult unconscious, which presumably explains the name. "Torpedo" derives from the Latin *torpidus*, meaning "numb or paralyzed," and the naval weapon took its name from the fish.

5. Crab

Crabs are decapods: They have ten legs, although the first two are claws. Many creatures called crabs, such as the horseshoe crab and hermit crab, are not true crabs. These can be easily identified because they have fewer legs than decapods. A crab's eyes are compound, made up of hundreds of lenses, and are set on stalks. These move in all directions, enabling the crab to see when hiding.

6. Fish

What is a fish? Many animals with names that end in "fish," such as crayfish, are not true fish. A true fish, or "fin fish," is an aquatic animal that has a backbone, fins, and gills throughout its life for breathing. The first such creature appeared about 530 million years ago. Today, we have identified more than 33,000 species, and of these, more than 1,700 face extinction.

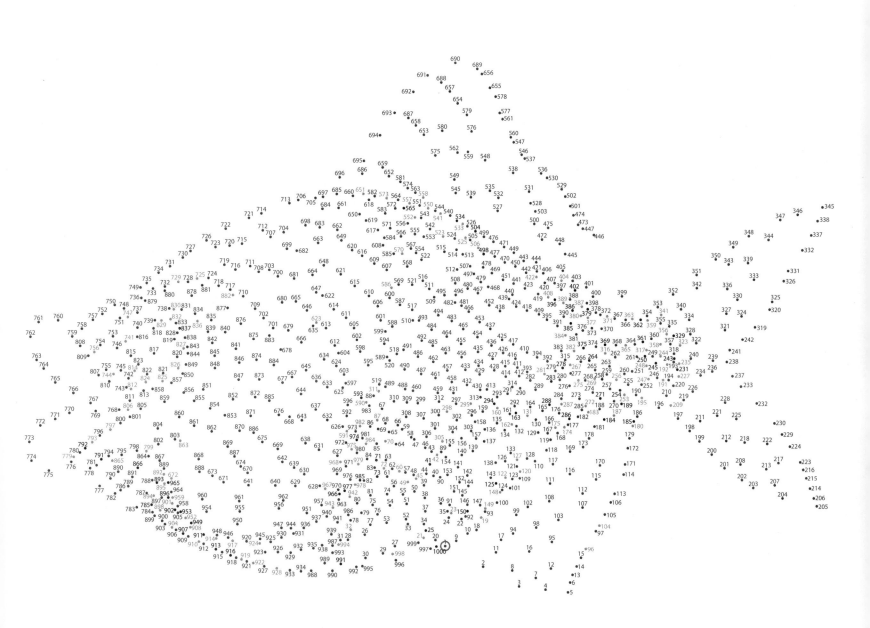

7. Shell

Most seashells come from mollusks, a group of marine animals that includes snails, mussels, and oysters. Shells are mostly made up of calcium carbonate, and the animals creating them take the calcium, carbon, and oxygen required from their food and the surrounding water. These ingredients are carried in the bloodstream to the mantle, an organ that secretes proteins that combine with the ingredients to create the shell.

8. Fish

Fins are perhaps the most distinctive feature of fish. Boney spines covered with skin, they help fish to turn, balance, and keep an upright position. Only the tail fin is involved with movement. Fish swim by contracting paired sets of muscles on each side of the backbone, which form ripples that move down its body to reach the tail fin, which propels the fish through the water.

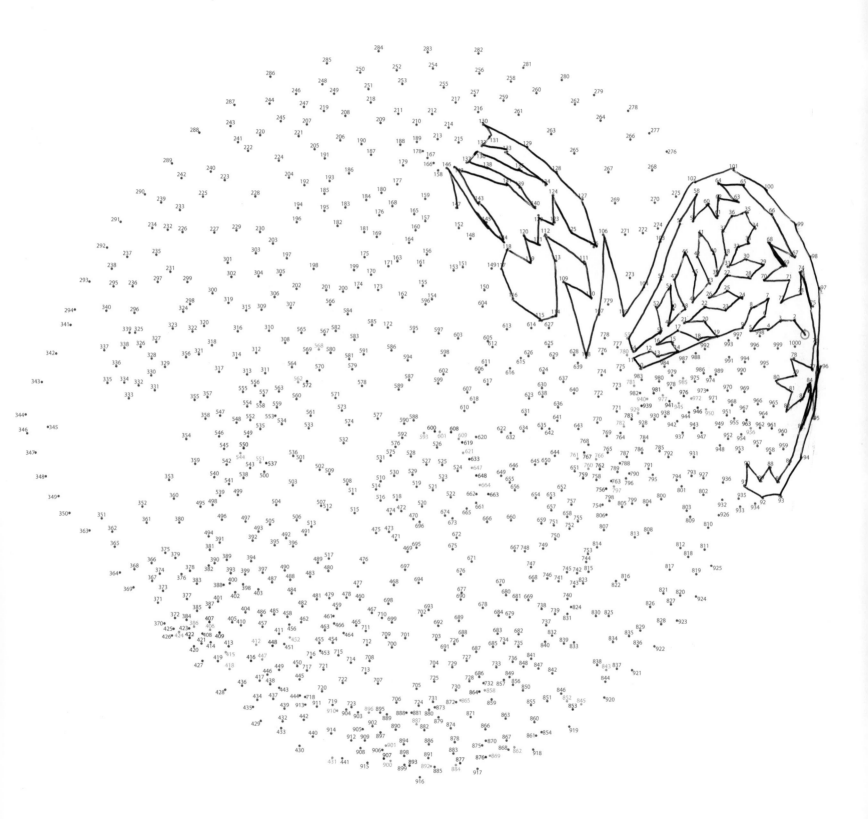

9. Shark

The modern shark first appeared about 100 million years ago, and today there are more than 500 species. The dwarf lantern shark is the smallest, at less than 7 inches (17 centimeters) long; the whale shark is the largest, at 40 feet (12 meters). Their teeth, so frightening in many species, are replaced throughout their lives. The teeth grow in a groove on the inside of the jaw and move forward as those in front are lost.

10. Fish

Why do fish have scales? Scales are hard plates that offer protection against the teeth of predators and sharp objects, such as coral. The scales overlap, so this "armor" does not prevent fish from bending and curling. The thin layer of skin that covers these scales contains glands that produce mucus, which makes fish feel slippery. It provides a barrier against bacteria and pollutants.

11. Whale

All whales have a thick layer of blubber. The main purpose is to provide insulation, and for those species living near the poles the layer can be 11 inches (28 centimeters) thick. A newly born whale calf has only a thin layer of blubber, but the mother's milk is rich in fat to enable it to develop more. The calf will drink about at least 100 gallons (380 liters) of milk every day.

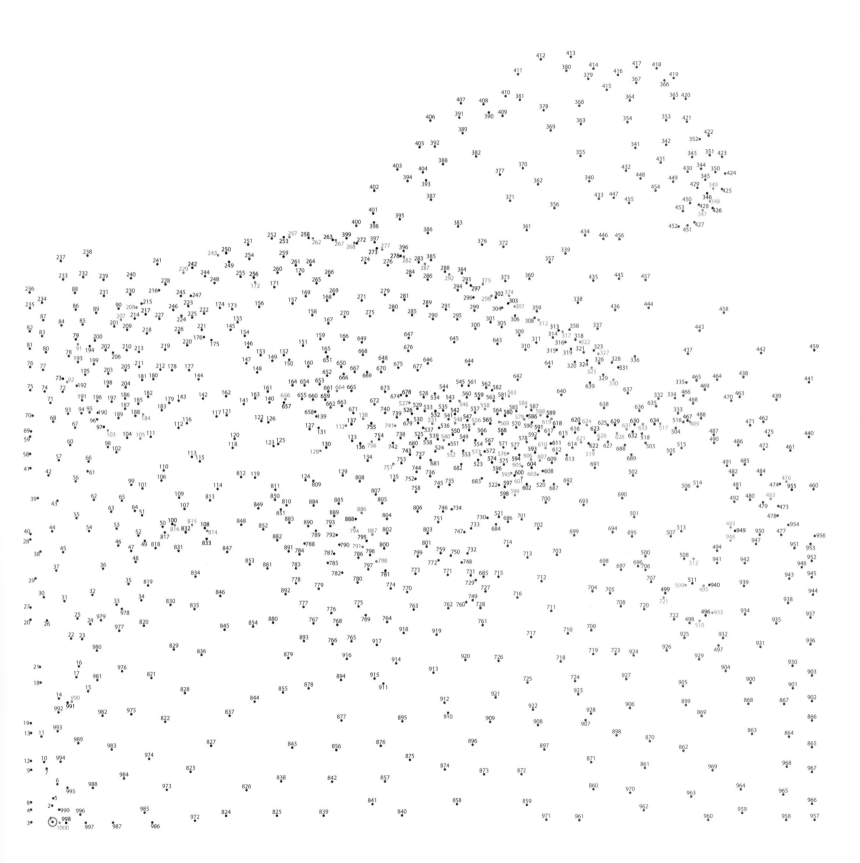

12. Stingray

As the name suggests, most stingrays have at least one stinger on their tail. Used only in self-defense, the stinger may be up to 14 inches (35 centimeters) long with serrated edges. The venom retains its strength even after the ray's death. Rays are not generally aggressive, and their instinct is usually to flee. Injuries to humans tend to occur after accidentally stepping on a ray buried in the sand.

13. Whale

We are familiar with images of whales lifting their tails out of the water and then slapping it down on the water's surface. What we don't know is why they do it. Called "lobtailing," it may be a sign of aggression or a warning of danger. "Breaching," in which the whale jumps clear out of the water, may be a form of play or it may help to dislodge parasites from the skin.

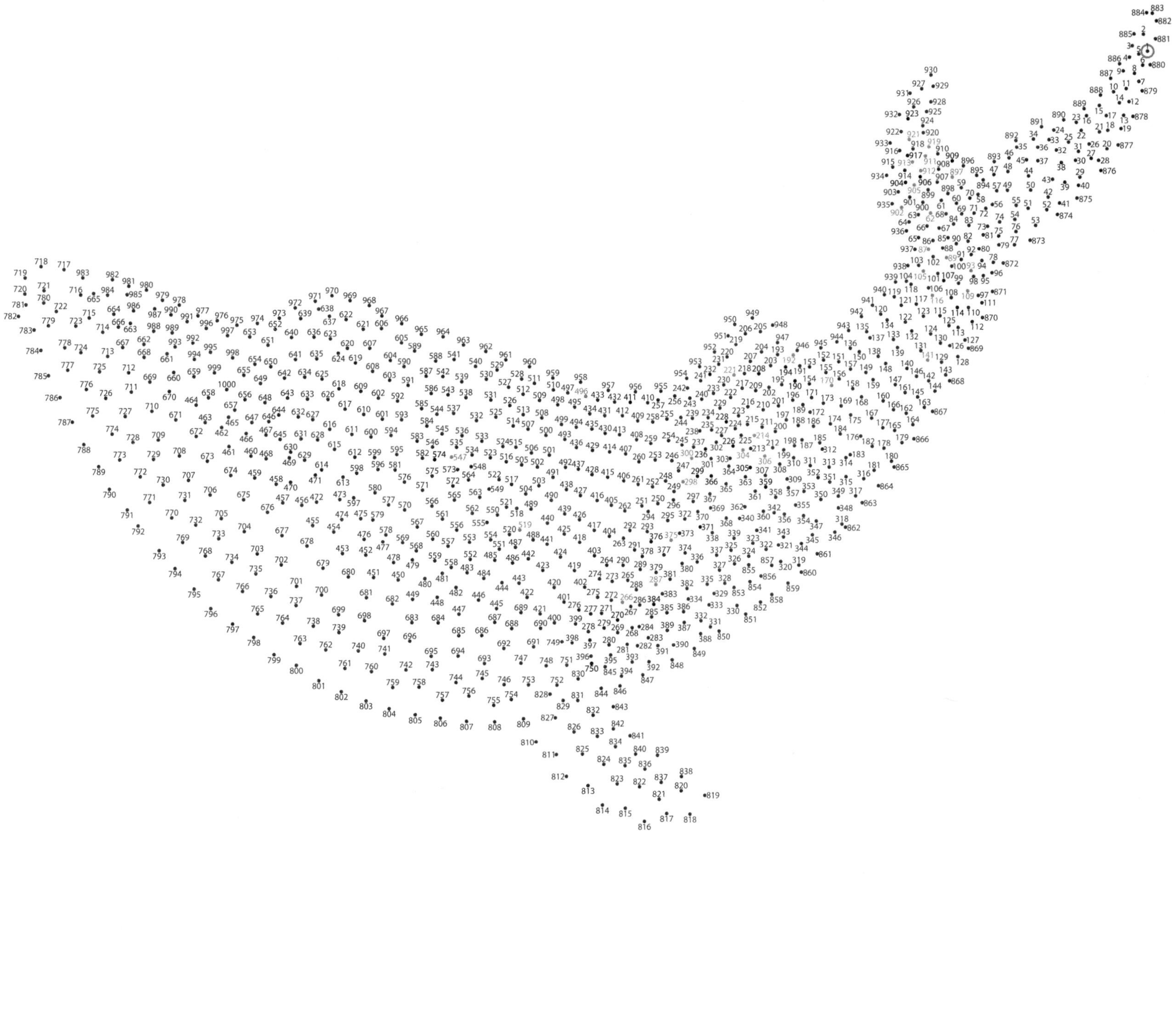

14. Sea Turtle

Sea turtles spend nearly all their lives in water. In fact, the only time a male is found on land is after he has hatched and is making a run for the sea. Females return to land only to lay their eggs. The result is that most of what we know about turtles concerns the behavior of the female laying her eggs, and of the hatchlings dashing for the sea.

15. Whale

Unlikely though it may seem, a new species of whale was discovered in 2014. The corpse of a whale had washed ashore on St. George Island, Alaska, and was initially believed to be a Baird's beaked whale. Yet it was too short to be an adult, but its teeth were yellowed and worn with age. DNA analysis confirmed this is a whale previously unknown to science.

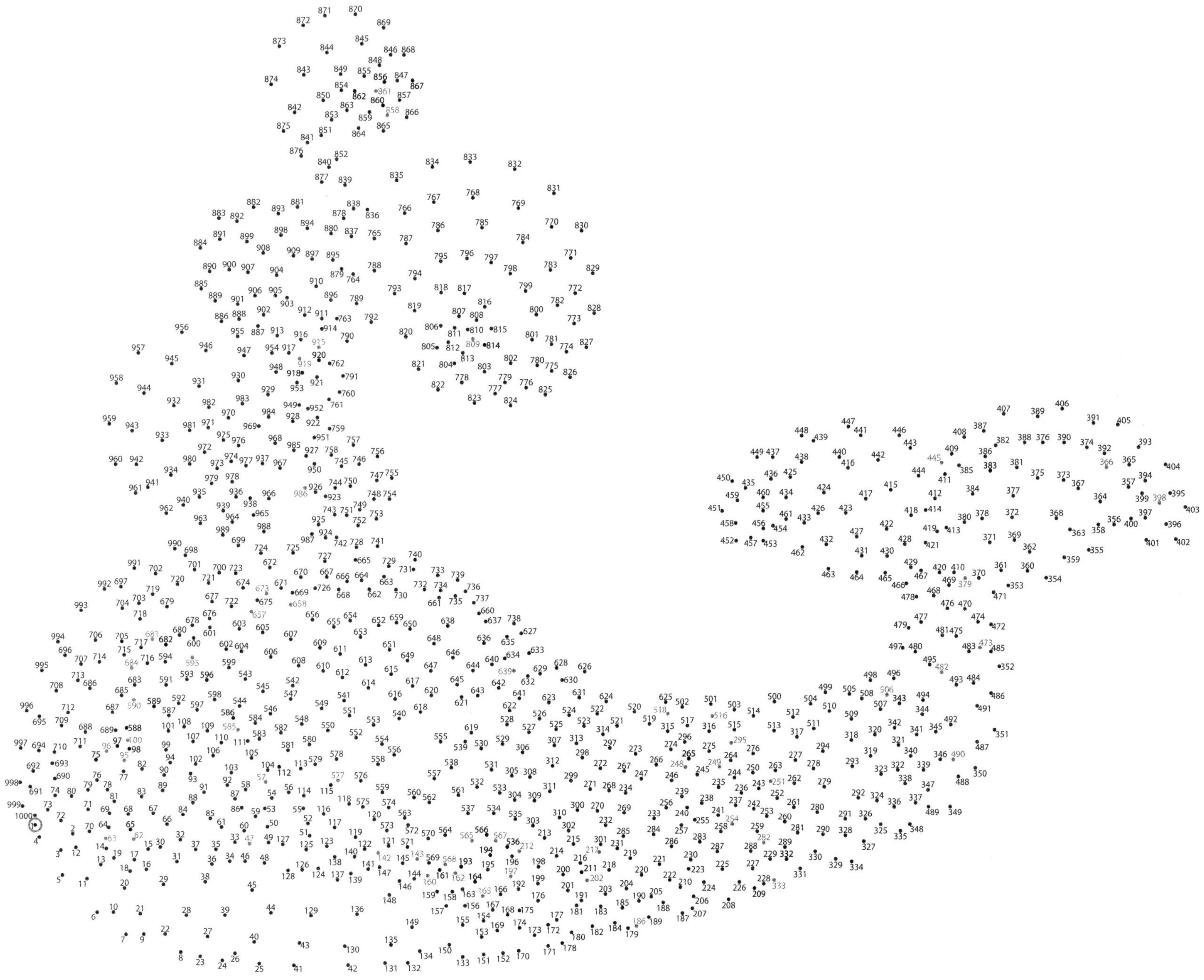

16. Shark

Sharks are a type of fish, with a skeleton made not of bone but of cartilage. Cartilage is flexible and about half the density of bone, which reduces the shark's overall weight and saves energy. For protection, their "skin" is made up of a series of scales, or dermal teeth, which act as an outer skeleton. Sharks have gills, but unlike other fish, these are not covered.

17. Stingray

Their eyes are on the top of their bodies, while their mouth and gills are underneath, so it is believed that stingrays do not rely on their vision when hunting. Instead, they rely on electroreceptors, gel-filled pits around their mouth, to pick up the electrical signals made when animals move. Stingrays feed mainly on mollusks and crustaceans, and some species have plates in their mouth to crush shells.

18. Crab

Crabs may group together to gather food or for protection. They use their claws, or chelae, for communication, either drumming with their pincers or waving. Some species of crabs can shed a claw that then regrows within a year. For this reason, some species are caught for food and their claws are twisted off their bodies before the crabs are returned live to the water. The assumption is that they will survive the experience.

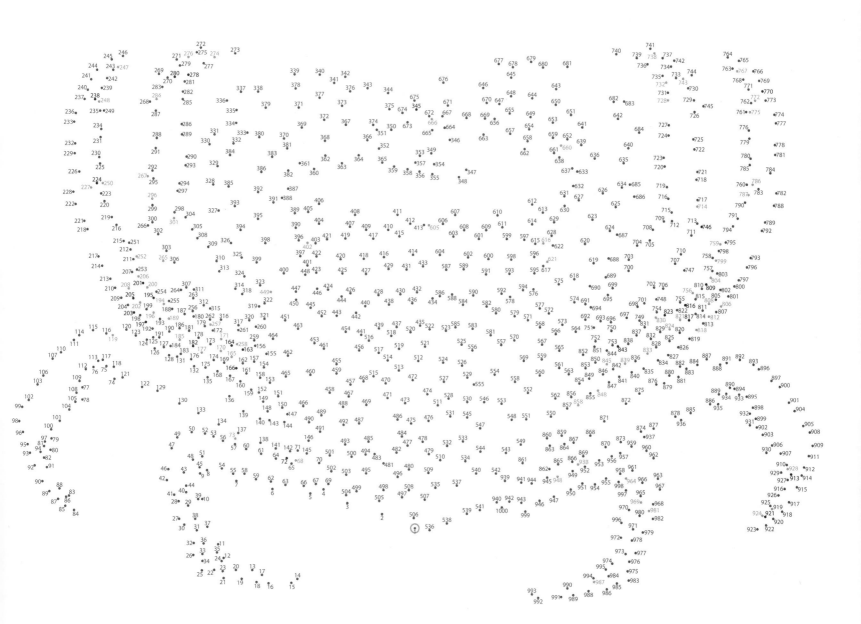

19. Octopus

The section cups on the arms of an octopus enable it to taste what it is touching. Tension sensors tell an octopus when its arms are stretched out, but not their position. What this means is that it must rely on its eyes to understand how it is moving its arms, as well as on chemical sensors in its suction cups to stop its arms from becoming entangled in each other.

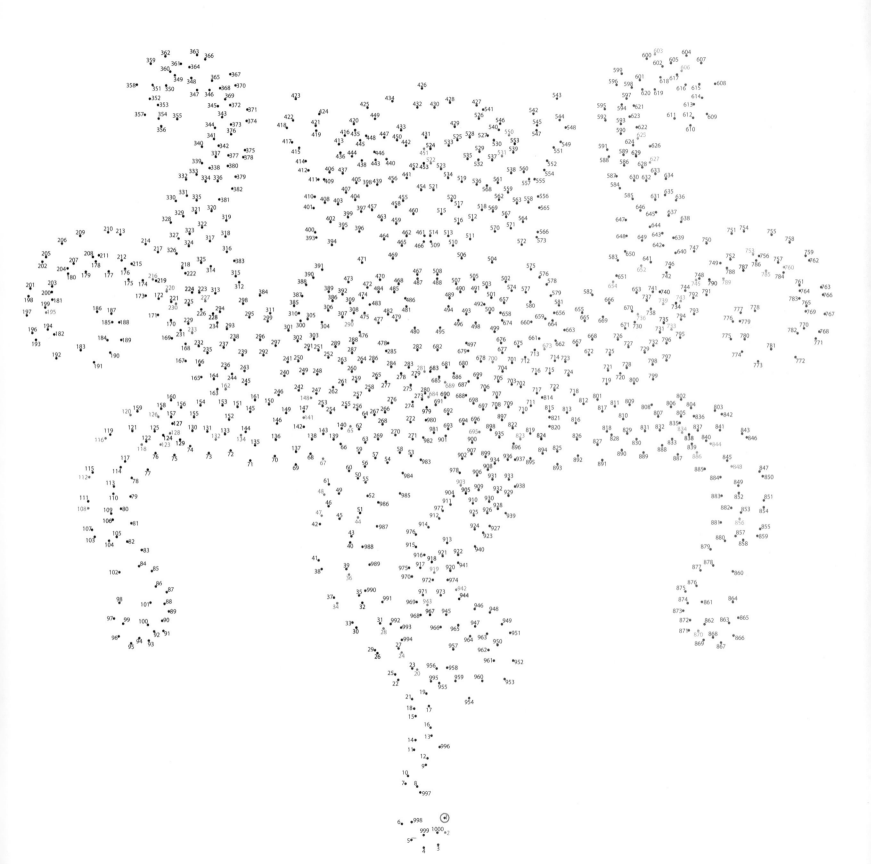

20. Lobster

Lobsters do not age like most other animals. They do not weaken or become less fertile, and they continue to molt throughout their lives. In fact, it is the process of molting itself that may lead to death. Molting requires energy, and up to 15 percent of lobsters die of exhaustion. Older lobsters may stop molting altogether, with the result that their shell degrades or even fractures.

21. Jellyfish

Because they do not have a backbone, jellyfish are not true fish, so the names "jellies" or "sea jellies" are preferred. These aquatic animals are more than 95 percent water, and they vary in size from a pinhead to larger than a human. Their "nerve net" enables them to sense a change in their environment and tells them whether they are facing up or down.

22. Fish

The structure of a fish's eye is similar to a human's. The most profound difference is the lens. Thick and shaped like a marble, it offers perfect vision underwater. Swordfish hunt in the dark, at an average depth of 1,800 feet (550 meters), so their eyes are larger than a baseball. Some fish that hunt in low light or even complete darkness rely on electric receptors to "see."

23. Sea Turtle

An adult sea turtle has few predators. Sharks and crocodiles are their biggest threat. It is the baby sea turtles that are most vulnerable. A female lays around 100 eggs, but of these only one will probably survive into adulthood. The nests may be raided, and within minutes of hatching they make easy prey. Once they reach the water, hatchlings may be preyed upon by large fish, seabirds and other turtles.

24. Shark

A female shark may lay eggs. She may carry her eggs within her body, which then hatch and are born, or she may give birth. Pups gestating inside the mother's body develop teeth and then cannibalize their developing siblings. As soon as pups are born, they swim away from their mother. This may be to avoid being eaten.

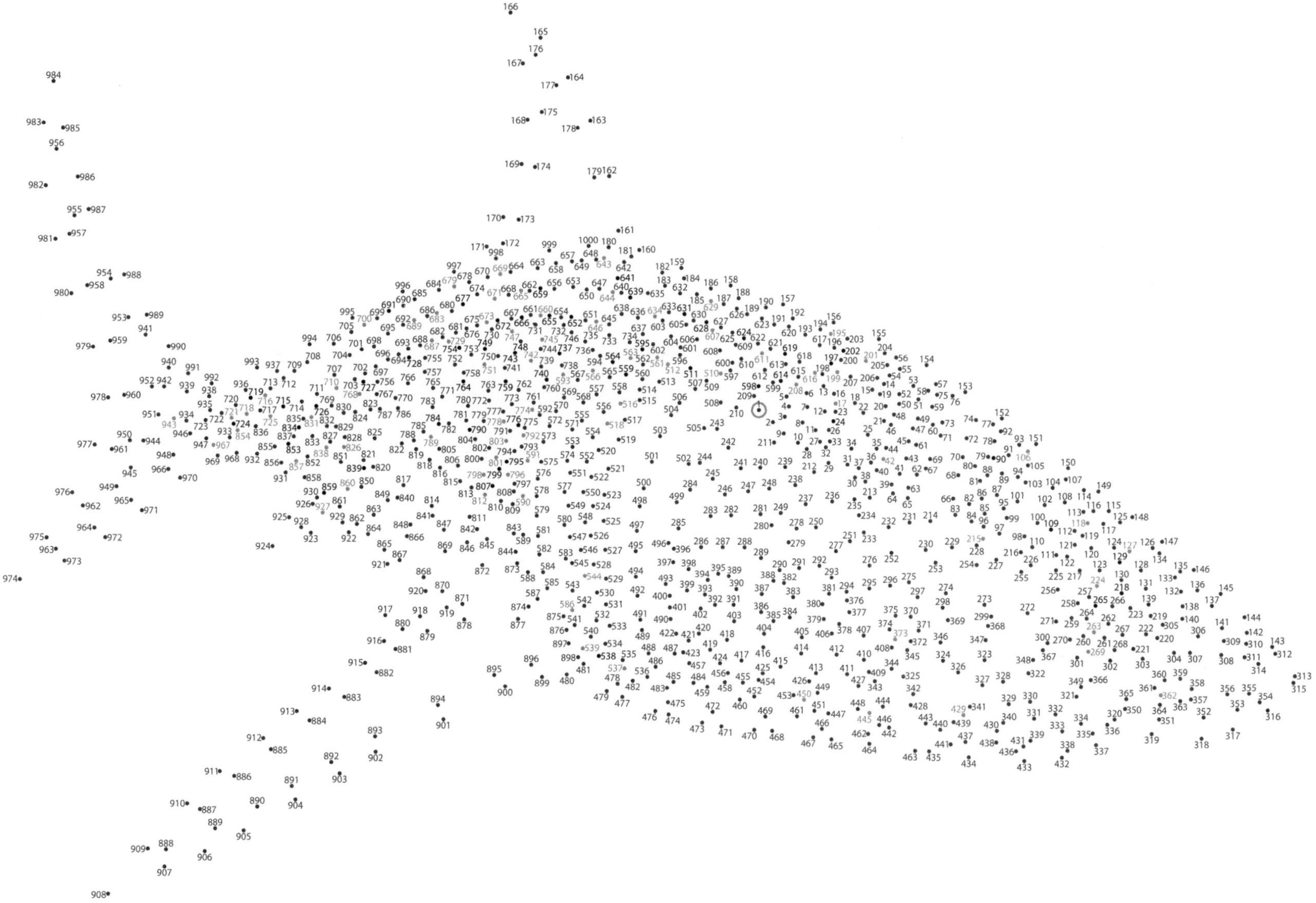

25. Whale

Contrary to popular belief, whales do not blow water from their blowhole. They're simply expelling the air they breathed in before diving. Warmed by the whale's body heat, it condenses on meeting the cooler air outside, which is why it looks like a spout of water. Every species of whale has a blowhole of a different shape, so their spouts also have a different shape, enabling whale watchers to identify the species.

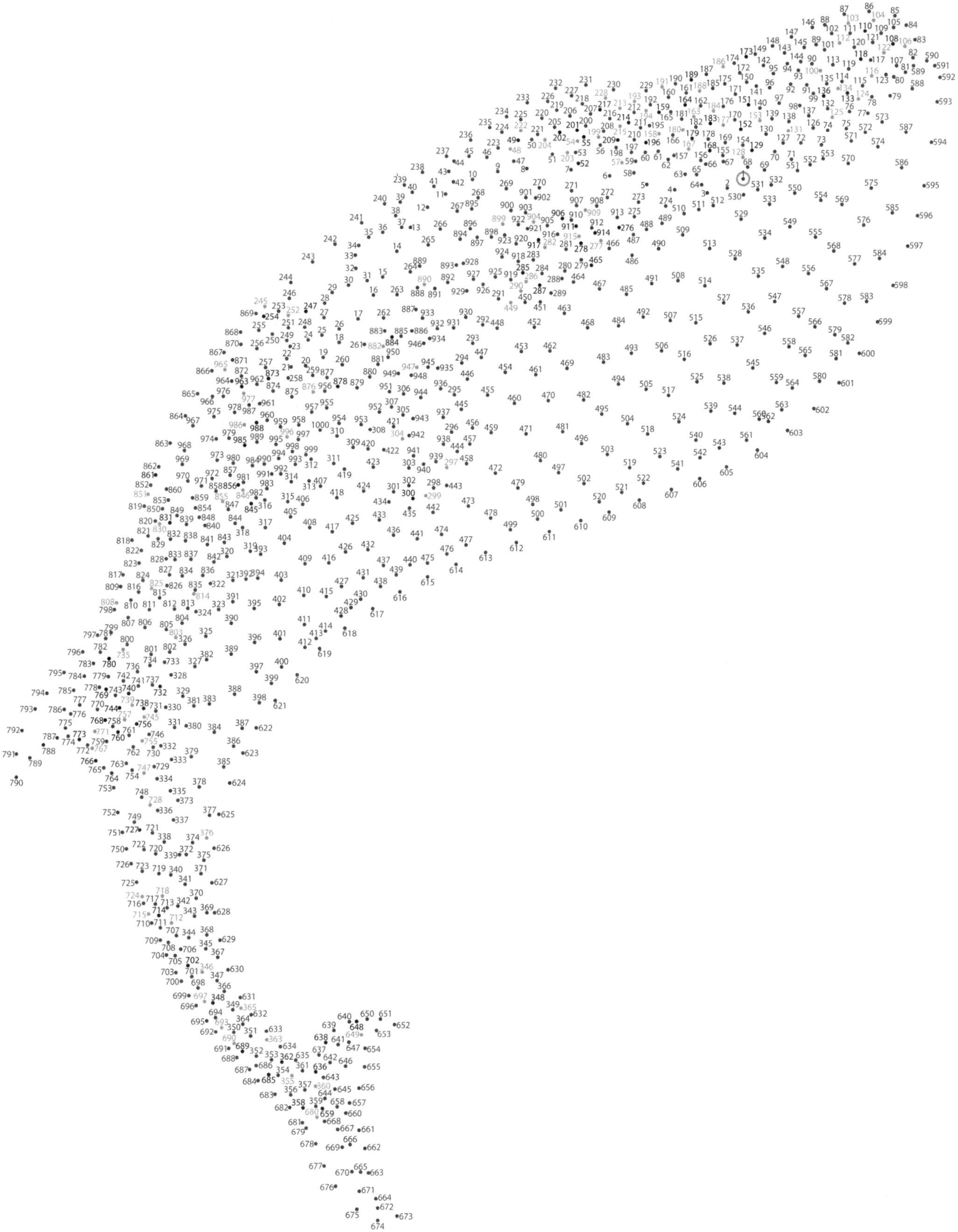

26. Lionfish

With its red, white, or black stripes, the lionfish offers a clear warning: "Don't touch!" This is an aggressive and poisonous species that delivers its venom from 18 needlelike dorsal fins. It is unlikely to kill an adult, but children are frequent victims. The lionfish is native to the Indo-Pacific but has established itself in the Caribbean and the East Coast of the United States.

27. Sea Turtle

Sea turtles have lungs and must, therefore, breathe air. Because they spend most of their time underwater, they must hold their breath for extended periods. A turtle looking for food may spend up to 40 minutes underwater, while a sleeping turtle may be underwater for up to seven hours. When it finally surfaces, it can refill its large lungs with one single breath out followed by a rapid breath in.

28. Fish

The lateral line is a system of sense organs that enable fish to detect movement in water and therefore detect predators and prey. Think of it as ears, eyes, and touch rolled into one. The system helps fish to orient themselves, vital for fish that travel in schools. Lateral lines are often just visible, running lengthwise on each side, from near the gill covers to the base of the tail fin.

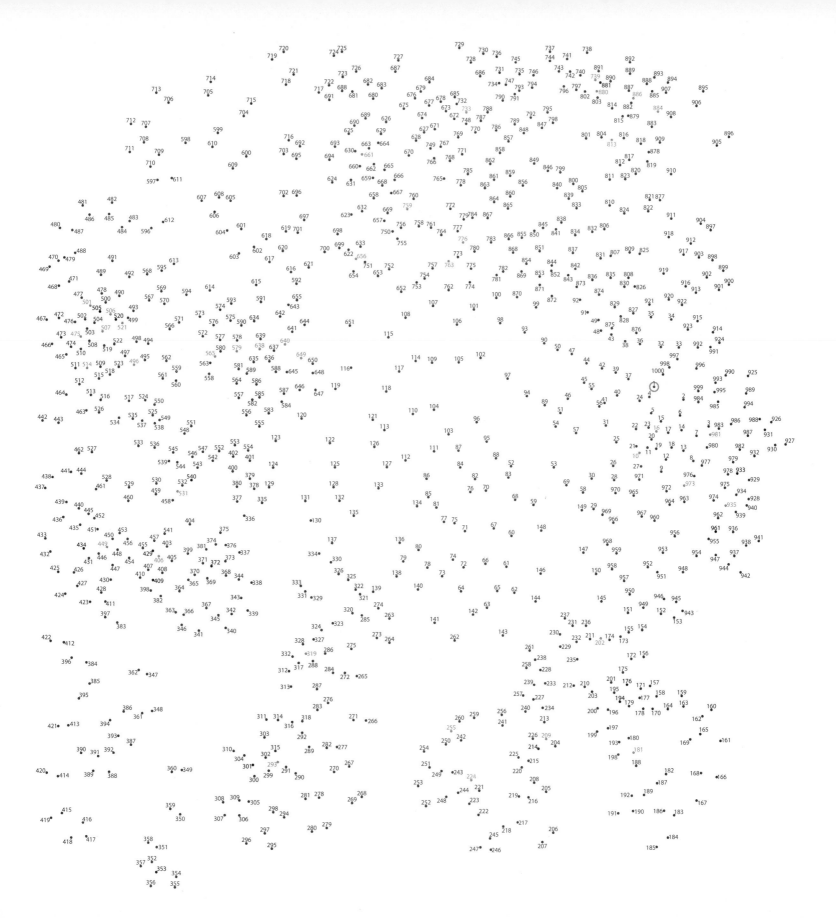

29. Fish

Do fish sleep? That's a surprisingly hard question to answer. Certainly there are moments when fish rest, but they seem to always remain alert to danger. Some fish become motionless; others secure themselves in mud or coral. And some, such as tuna and mackerel, never stop moving. Research suggests that it is possible to keep moving even while parts of the brain are less active.

30. Fish

Sound waves travel through water and are sensed by a fish's hearing organs, located within the skull. They enable the fish to respond even when it can't see. For example, a trout in a river that is regularly fished will flee at the sound of human footsteps. Fish communicate with each other by producing sounds, whether by using their swim bladders or rasping their teeth.

31. Cowrie Shell

The shells of cowries are usually rounded and shiny. So shiny, in fact, that the word "porcelain" derives from the Italian for cowrie, *porcellana*. Cowrie shells have long been used for jewelry, and also as a form of currency. Cowrie shell money was important for trade across Africa and was legal tender in some areas until the mid-nineteenth century. It was also used in China, where the classical character for "money" is a stylized cowrie.

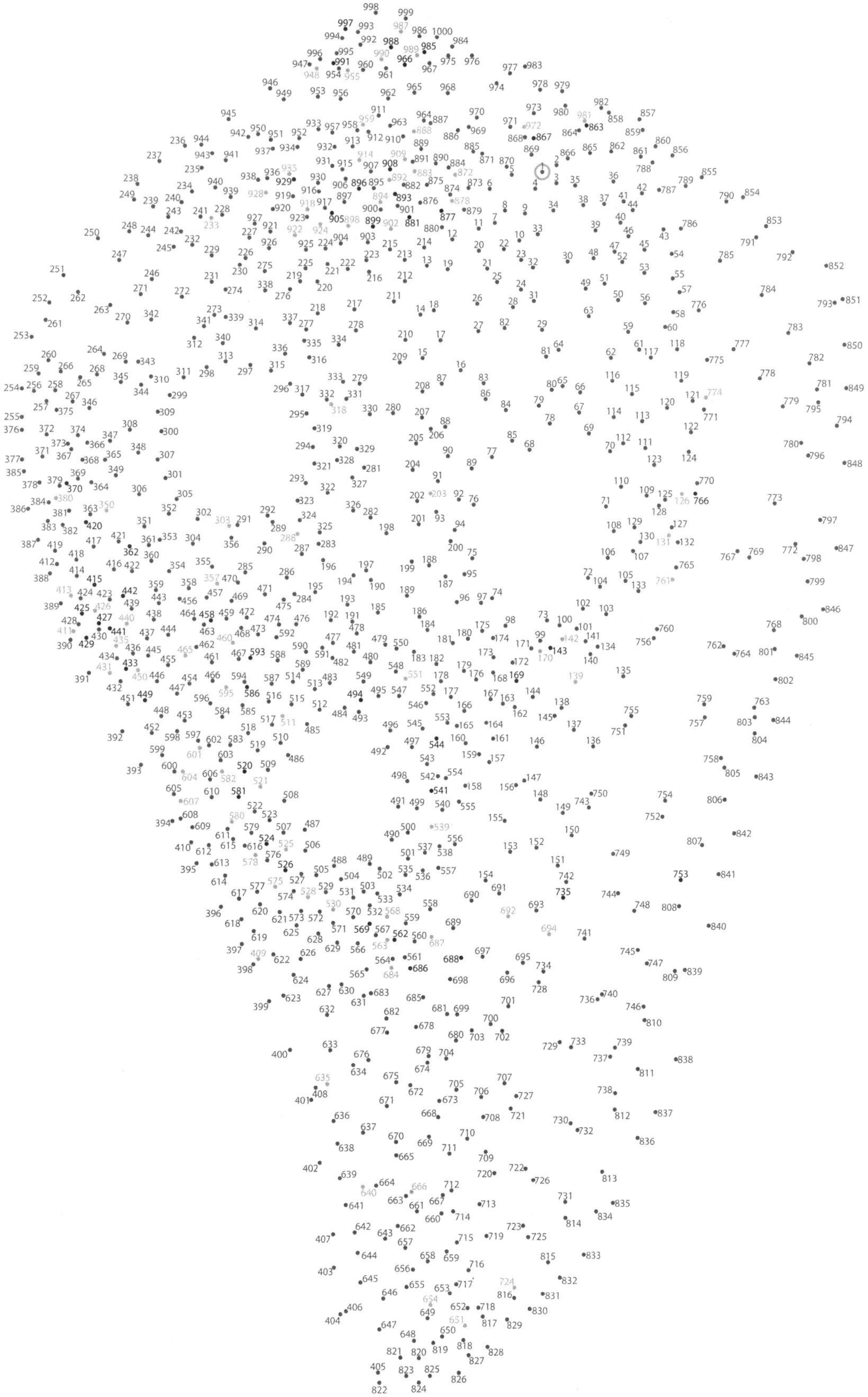

32. Shell

Colors and patterns on shells may serve a purpose. It's possible they help mollusks to place their mantles correctly to continue making their shells. Similarly, ridges and spikes are not mere ornamentation. They create an armor that's difficult for predators to break through. They may also help to stop a mollusk from sinking into sand or mud. By contrast, a smooth shell helps a snail to move quickly and without being noticed.

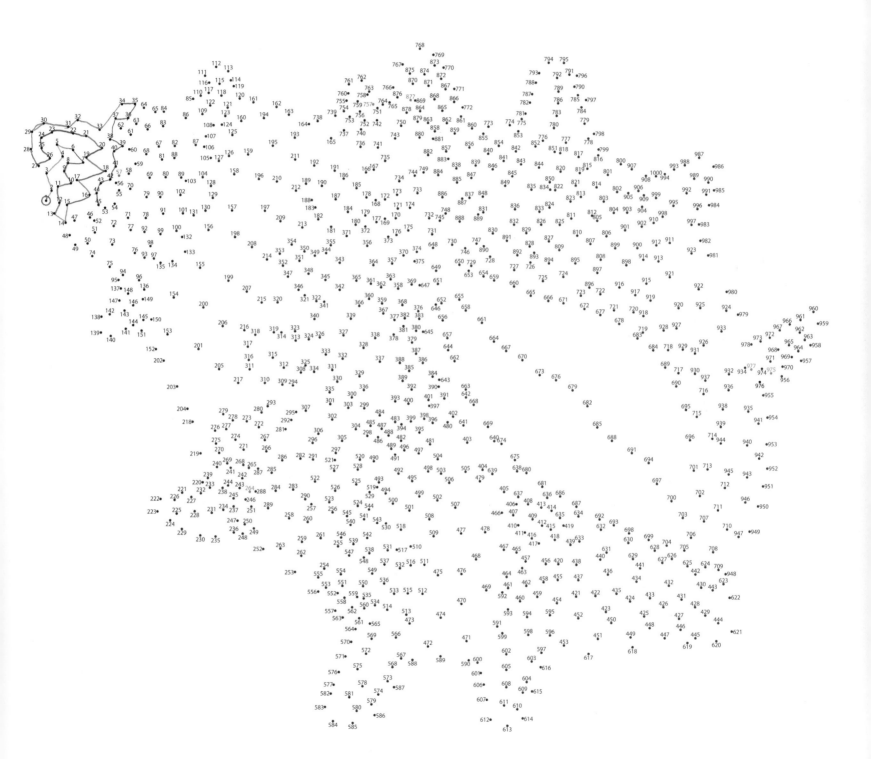

33. Starfish

Starfish are not fish; they are marine invertebrates. Most species have five arms, and at the end of these are eyes that can sense light and dark. On the underside of the arms are hundreds of tube feet. By contracting and relaxing its muscles, the sea star forces water in and out of its feet, enabling movement. However, starfish are not speedy: about 6 inches (15 centimeters) a minute is average.

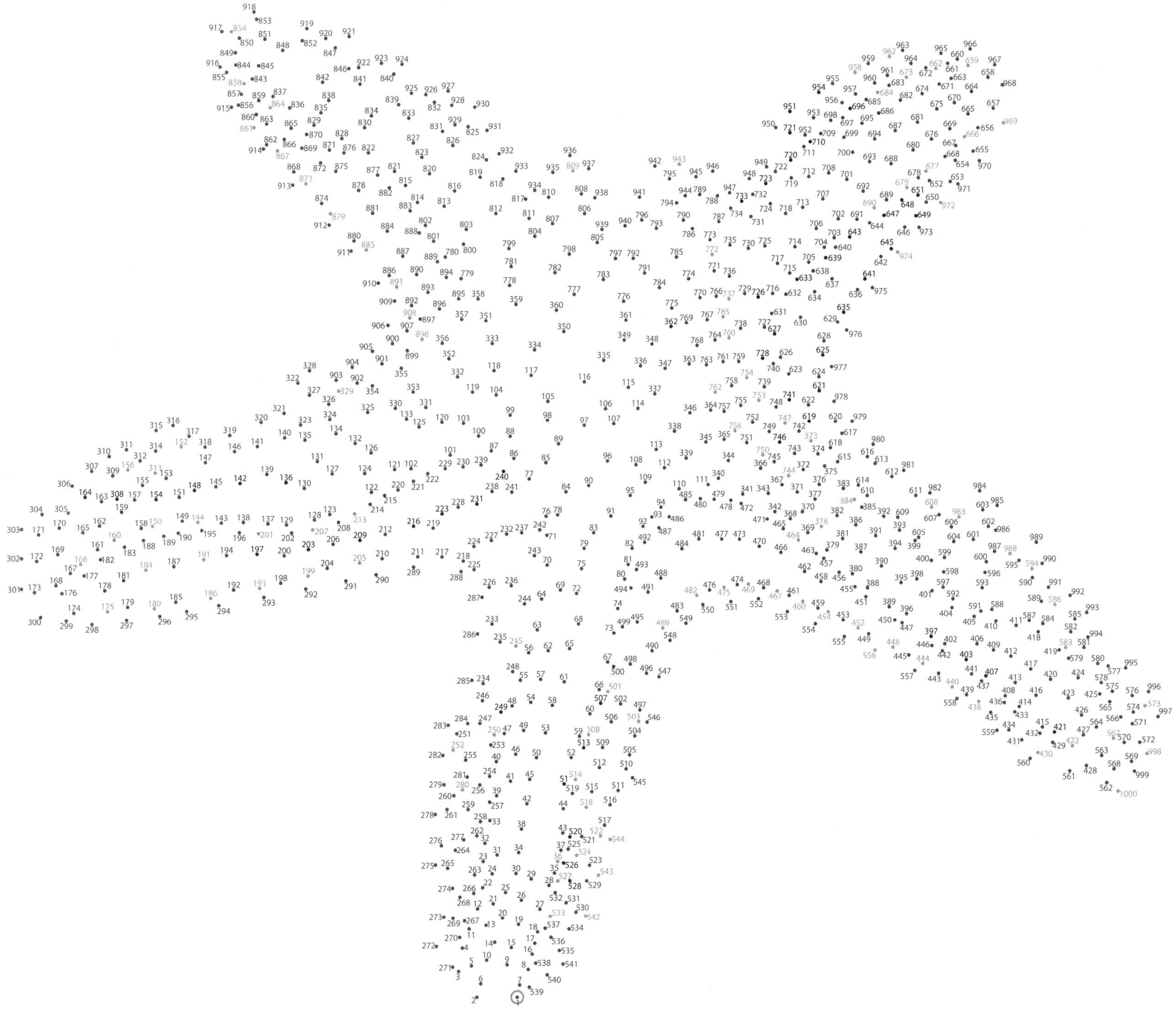

34. Crab

Because their hard shell, or exoskeleton, cannot grow with them, crabs must molt. About a day before, the crab will absorb seawater, which causes it to swell. This helps to expand the old shell and force it apart. The crab must then extract itself from the shell, a process that can take hours. It must then hide for the next few days until the new shell hardens.

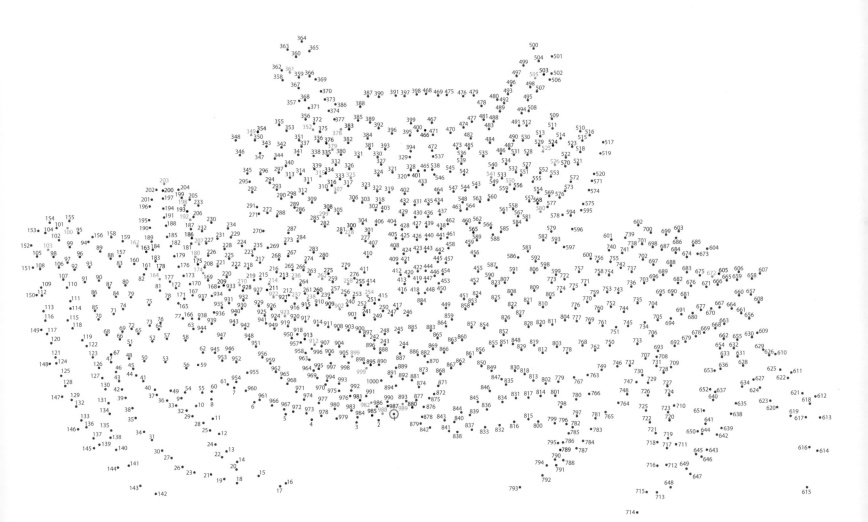

35. Sea Horse

The male sea horse is the only creature to take full responsibility for incubating the young. The reason seems to be that the generation of eggs is costly for the female. In one cycle, she will deposit up to 1,500 eggs in the male's pouch, and these will weigh up to one third of her body weight. The male releases the young between 9 and 45 days later, but less than 0.5 percent will survive.

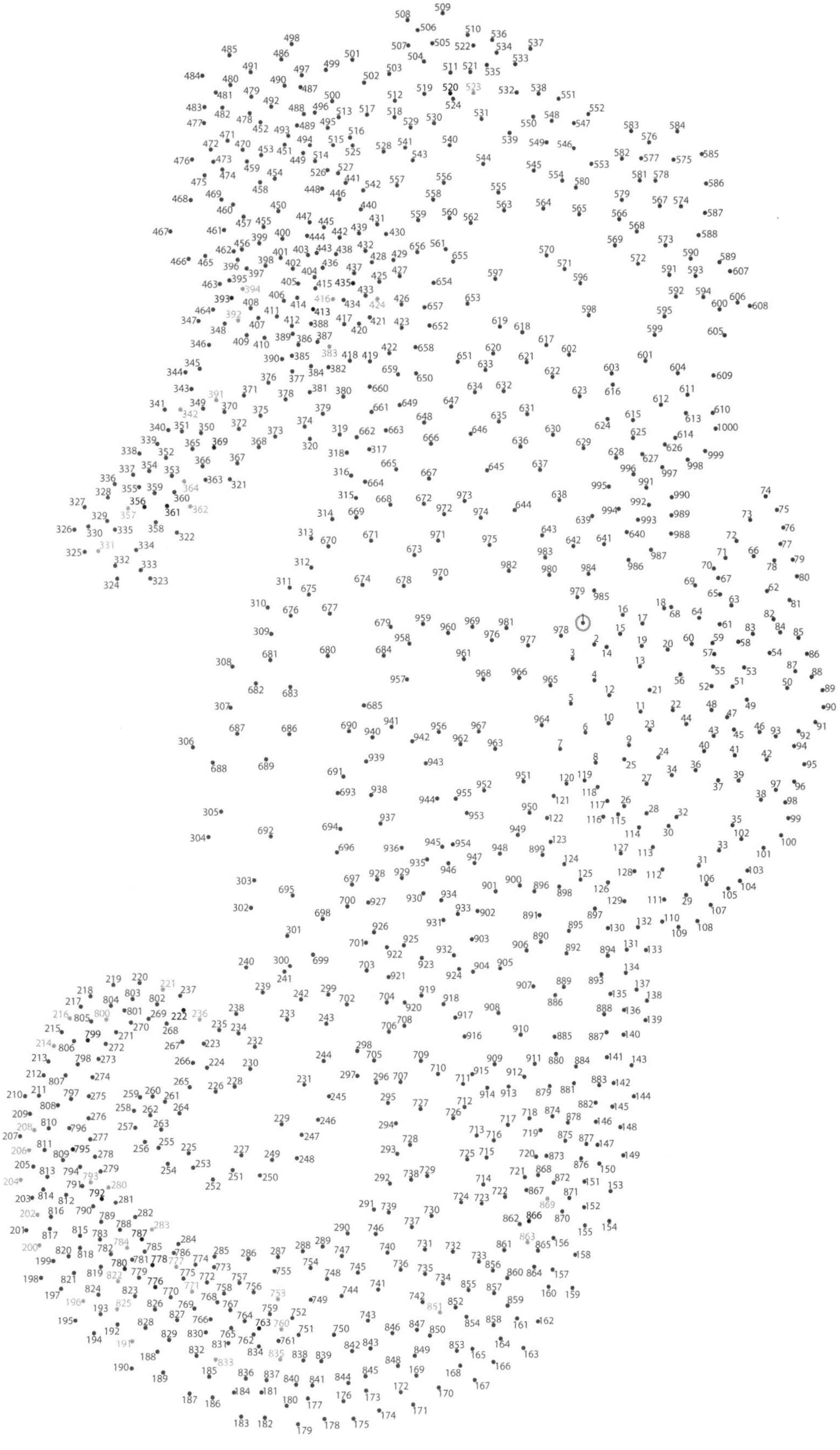

36. Crab

There are around 4,500 species of true crabs. The smallest, the pea crab, is about the size of a pea. It lives as a parasite within clams, oysters, and mollusks, and it is dependent on its host for food and protection. The largest, the Japanese spider crab, measures up to 18 feet (5.5 meters) from claw to claw. It looks monstrous but has a gentle disposition.

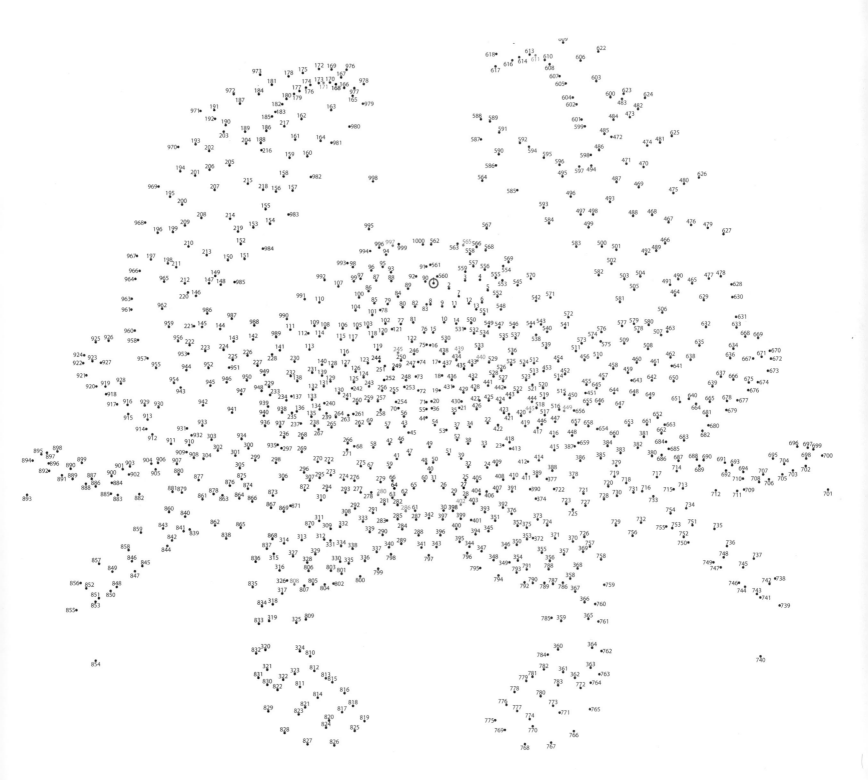

37. Fish

Science has explored only 1 percent of the ocean depths. How many more fish remain to be discovered? In 1938, a fisherman off the east coast of South Africa caught a strange-looking fish. Scientists eventually realized it was a coelacanth, a fish assumed to have become extinct around 66 million years ago. In fact, it lives deep in the Indian Ocean, where it has few predators.

38. Octopus

Their brain is only the size of a walnut, but octopuses are highly intelligent and have been seen using tools. Several species pick up coconut shells and use them for shelter. Others use stones to camouflage the entrance to their den. The development of intelligence may have been a response to losing their shell. Octopuses are descended from a shell-bearing mollusk that appeared around 500 million years ago.

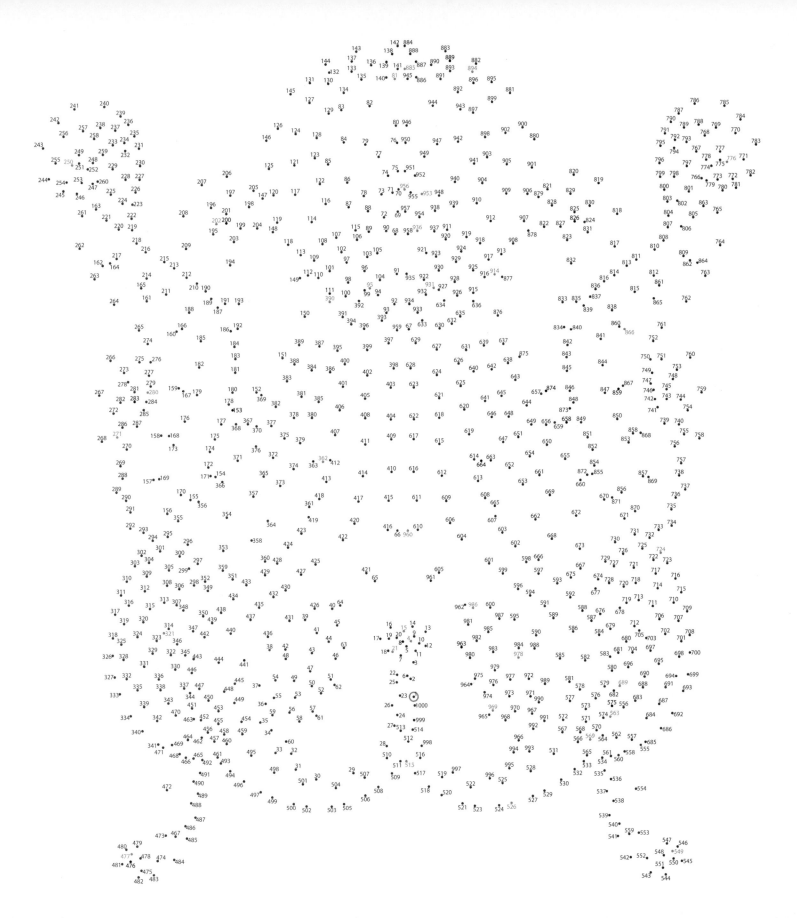

39. Conch

The conch is the shell of medium-to-large sea snails. Two pairs of tentacles on the head enable the snail to detect light and feel and touch. The shell can be used as a wind instrument by cutting a hole in the spire, close to the apex, and then blowing into the shell. The queen conch may sometimes produce pearls in various colors. Pink is particularly prized.

40. Shark

The shark is an apex predator: It sits at the top or close to the top of the food chain. A decline in shark populations could have a catastrophic effect. Sharks tend to prey on sick or weak individuals, and also feed on carcasses. This means they help to prevent the spread of disease within their prey species and also strengthen its gene pool.

41. Lobster

Lobsters have two stomachs. The first is located behind its eyes and contains a gastric mill, with three teethlike features that crush its food. Once it is fine enough, the crushed food passes to the second stomach. Lobsters will scavenge, if necessary, and have been known to resort to cannibalism. However, lobster skin found in their stomach may not be evidence of this; they eat their own shells after molting.

42. Octopus

Reproduction is the last thing a female octopus does. Depending on the species, she lays up to 200,000 eggs. She then cares for them until they hatch, protecting them from predators and blowing water over them to ensure a plentiful supply of oxygen. The incubation period varies from two to ten months, during which time she will not eat. Death follows shortly after the eggs hatch.

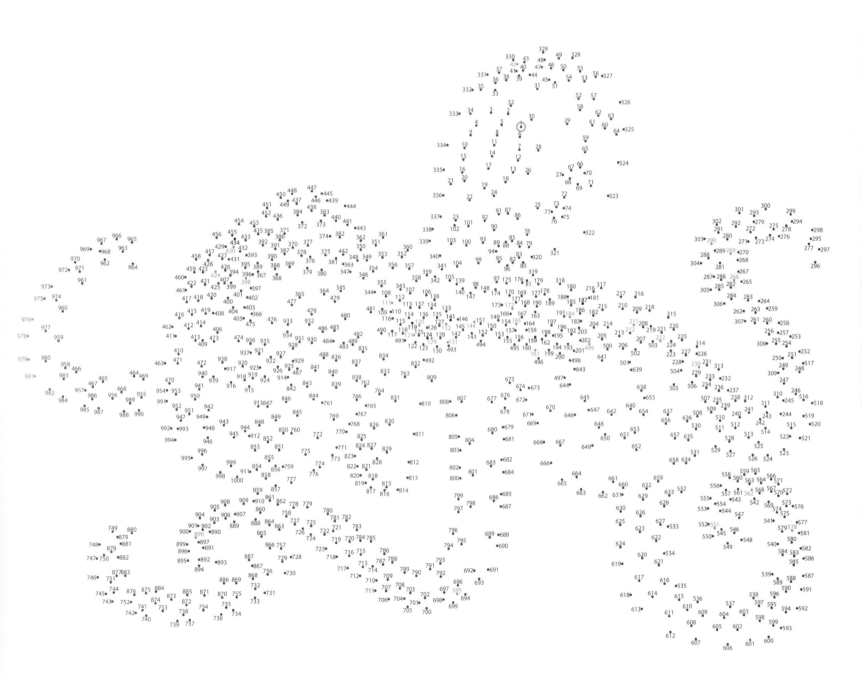

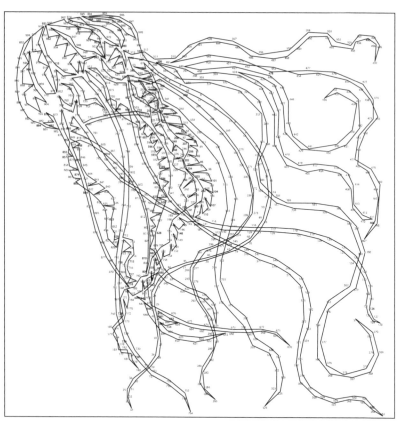

1. Jellyfish

2. Sea Horse

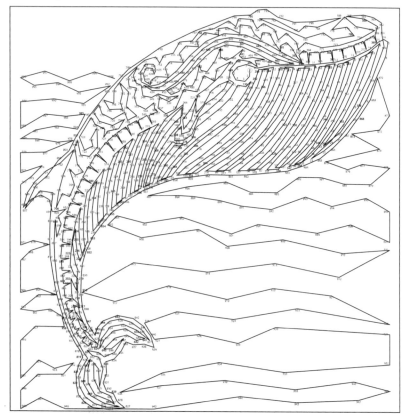

3. Blue Whale

4. Torpedo Ray

5. Crab

6. Fish

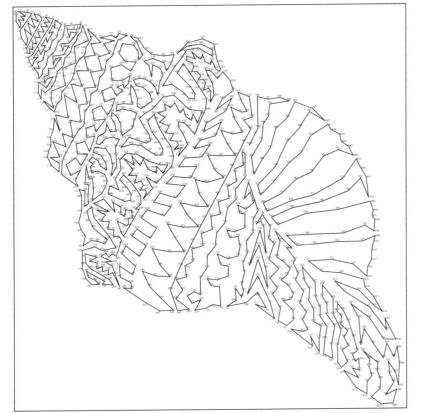

7. Shell

8. Fish

9. Shark

10. Fish

11. Whale

12. Stingray

13. Whale

14. Sea Turtle

15. Whale

16. Shark

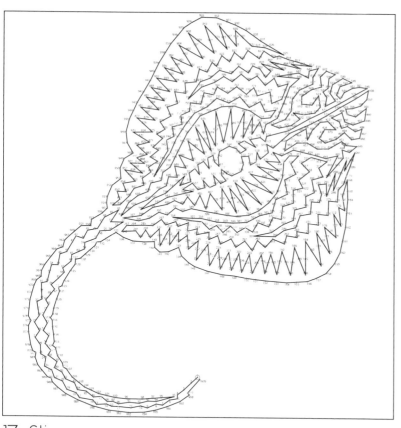

17. Stingray

18. Crab

19. Octopus

20. Lobster

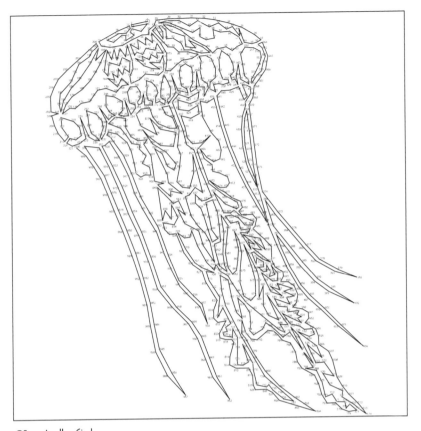

21. Jellyfish

22. Fish

23. Sea Turtle

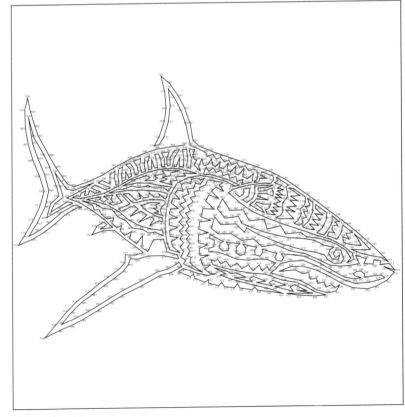

24. Shark

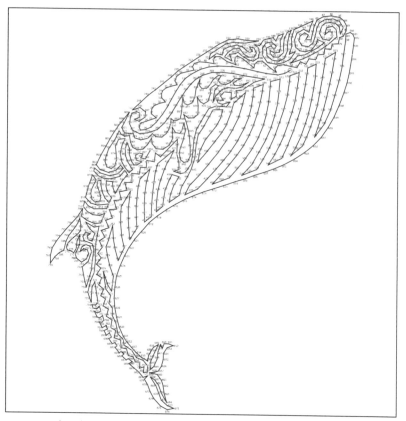

25. Whale

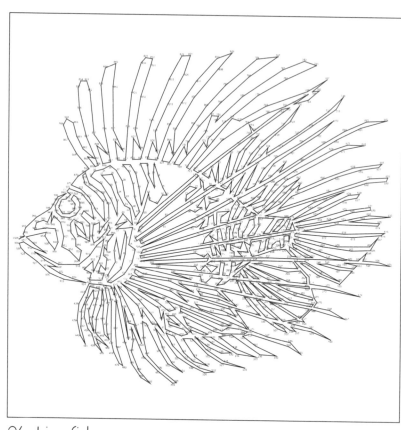

26. Lionfish

27. Sea Turtle

28. Fish

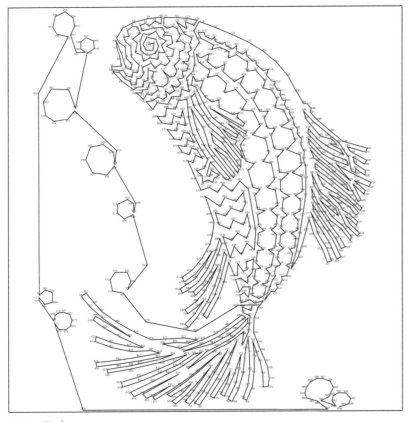

29. Fish

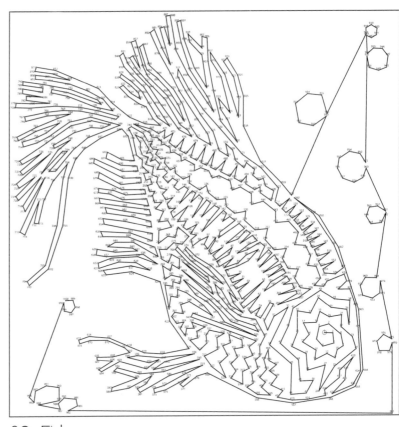

30. Fish

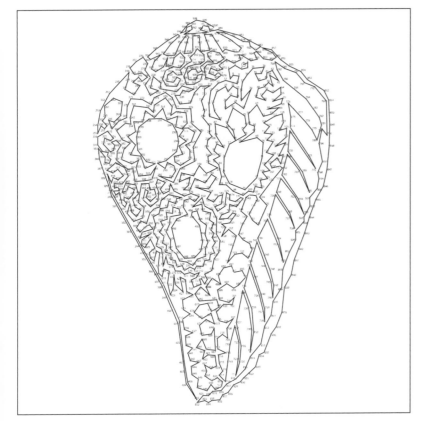

31. Cowrie Shell

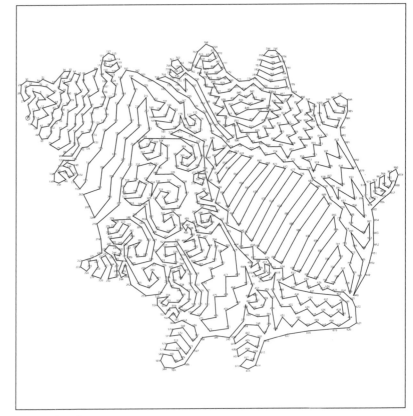

32. Shell

33. Starfish

34. Crab

35. Sea Horse

36. Crab

37. Fish

38. Octopus

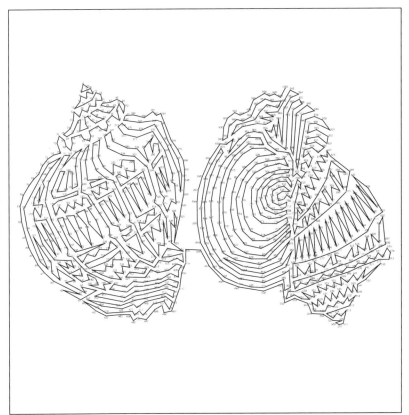

39. Conch

40. Shark

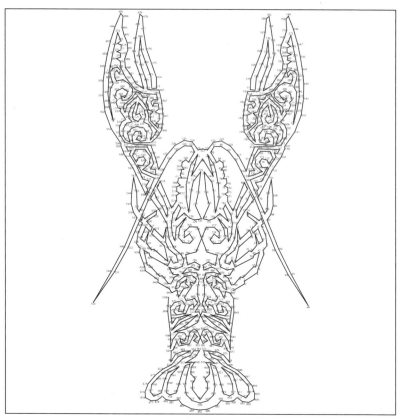

41. Lobster

42. Octopus

THIS IS A SEVENOAKS BOOK

Published by Carlton Books Ltd
20 Mortimer Street
London W1T 3JW

Copyright © 2017 Carlton Books Ltd

A CIP catalogue record for this book is available from the British Library

2 4 6 8 10 9 7 5 3 1

ISBN 978-1-78177-593-6

Printed in China

All images supplied by Shutterstock.com